Best of
More
GOODNIGHT STORIES

TINY TOT PUBLICATIONS
INDIA

Best of
More

GOODNIGHT
STORIES

© TINY TOT PUBLICATIONS 2009
This Edition:- 2014

Edited by:
Shyam Dua
Published By:
TINY TOT PUBLICATIONS
H-37,Sector-63
Noida-201301
(G.B. Nagar) (U.P.)
Ph.: 9310163582, 9310167314, 0120-4251898
Fax.:011-22167314
Regd. Office:
235, Jagriti Enclave, Delhi-110092 (INDIA)
Ph.: 011-42427727
email:tinytotpub@hotmail.com
ISBN : 81-304-0634-9

Illustrated by
Bookmark

CONTENTS

THE YOUNGEST WATER FAIRY

Long ago, the king of sea was living in the sea with his wife and five daughters. The daughters were very beautiful but the youngest one was the most beautiful. She was a good singer as well. When she sang all the creatures of water would hear her. But she had not seen the world outside the sea. So, she was very keen to see the outside world.

One day, she said to her mother, "I want to see the outside world like my sisters. When will I be able to see humans, sun, moon etc."

"You are too young to go out. When you will be fifteen years old your father will allow you to go out of the sea. Your sisters also were able to go out only when they turned fifteen." said her mother.

"Then the period of my wait is going to be over as I will be fifteen this year only." youngest fairy chirped.

At last the most awaited day arrived. The fairy was

extremely happy that day.

On her birth day her father allowed her to go out of the sea and said, "You can go out but remember my advice to be cautious of humans. They may cause trouble to us. The world out of sea is not ours."

"Yes father. I will follow your advice." Saying this, the youngest fairy went out of the sea.

She swam up to the surface of the sea. She was happy for the first time to breath in the open air. She spoke to herself, "What a fine atmosphere! The blue sky looks wonderful." She sat on a rock by the sea side. She enjoyed the natural beauty of outside world. She was in a great mirth. Then she saw a ship coming towards her. It was decorated and looked very attractive in the light. The sound of sweet music was also heard from it.

The fairy saw the ship with great interest. She

thought, "Some celebration seems to be going on in there. Let me see what it is all about ."

She decided to go to the ship. But then she thought, "I am not like humans with this long tail." And she became sad.

As the ship reached nearer, she heard the voice coming from it, "Congratulation! Happy Birthday to you, Captain! Many happy returns of the day!"

She now understood that birth day of the captain was being celebrated. She saw the captain who was a handsome youth. She fell in love with him.

Suddenly the sky got overcast and thunder storm raised the high waves in the sea. The ship started

sinking. All the crew drowned in the sea. The captain was also going to get drowned but the water fairy saved him and brought him to the shore. As she couldn't walk on the ground, she went back to sea. She was seeing the unconscious captain from behind a rock in the sea praying for his recovery.

Then some girls appeared there. When they saw the captain, they tried to bring him to consciousness. After some time captain got up. Seeing a beautiful girl before him, he fell in love with her and said, "So, you have saved my life. I am obliged to you and have no words to express my gratitude."

The girl said, "Don't say so I found you lying

unconscious here. Whatever I did was my duty."

Then both of them parted from each other. The captain was quite unaware that the water fairy had saved his life. The youngest water fairy returned to sea. Her sisters came to meet her and asked, "How did you like the world outside the sea? What diet you see there?

The youngest fairy narrated all that had happened. Then, remembering the handsome captain tears came to her eyes. Her elder sister told her, "That world is not ours. What you are thinking cannot be possible. You have met a human for the first time, so you are feeling like this. You will forget him in the course of the time." Her other sisters also console her and asking her not to be sad for the impossible.

But the youngest water fairy was unable to forget the captain. She confined herself in her room. She continued to think about the captain. She seemed to have forgotten about herself. Though she knew that

a water fairy could not be married to a human being, even then she was not able to forget him. At last, she remembered the water fairy magician and decided to go to her.

"She met the magician without informing any one. The water fairy magician said to her, "Hello, my dear water fairy. What brought you here to me?"

The fairy narrated all the story and said, "I want human legs in place of tail. Please help me."

"Do you know what you are asking for. It is not good to sacrifice your own identity for a human," said the water fairy magician.

But the youngest fairy was stuck to her demand, "Do something so that I may acquire human legs instead of this tail." All right. I will do that for you but there would be a problem. Whenever, you will put your feet

on ground, you'll have an acute pain," said the water fairy magician.

"I will bear every thing for him. I have to go to him," said the fairy.

"But you have to pay for my service," said the water fairy magician.

"What do you want? I am ready to give anything." said the fairy.

"I need your sweet voice," said the water fairy magician. "You will no longer be able to speak. Moreover, if the youth marries some other woman, then you will not be able to live in water because you will have lost the form of water fairy."

"Okay! I accept the condition," said the fairy.

The water fairy magician gave a potion to her and said, "Drink the potion after reaching the sea shore."

The fairy took the potion and swam fast towards a

shore. As soon as she reached the shore, she drank the potion. Soon with a severe pain, her tail was replaced by human legs. She became unconscious due to the pain. When she regained senses, she saw the captain who was infect a prince in front of her. This is what she wanted. Now she was very happy.

The prince said, "Do not be afraid. You are safe now. But tell me who you are and where you are coming from?"

The water fairy tried to speak but she couldn't as her voice was no more. She merely smiled.

"Well, come to my palace," said the prince. "You will be comfortable there."

Water fairy went to the palace. She started a new life there. She would wear precious clothes, enjoy horse riding and participate in different functions with the prince. Despite acute pain in every step she took she was happy to be in the company of the prince. But she was unable to express her love to him. The prince was unaware of the feelings of the fairy. He was in love with the girl whom he had met on the shore. Though he never met her again yet he always thought of her.

One day, a ship stopped at his port. The prince went to meet the people with the fairy. He was surprised to see the same girl who had saved his life. He went to her and began talking to her. Seeing this the fairy was shocked. She thought that she would never be able to get the prince. She was observing every thing like a statue.

The prince proposed the girl to marry him. The girl agreed as she had also been in love with him.

After some days the marriage was performed with great pomp and show. The fairy was very sad. After marriage the prince and his wife decided to go on a

voyage. A big ship was made for the voyage. They also forced water fairy to go with them.

During the journey, one night, the fairy was very sad. She was recollecting the words of the water magician. She decided to finish her life. She was about to jump into the water when she heard the sound of weeping. She saw her sisters, coming towards her. They were all very sad. They came to her and said, "We all love you. Why did you fall in love with a human. The water fairy magician has told every thing to us. Now she has sent us to save you. Here is a magic knife, kill the prince by this knife and you will become water fairy again."

"But your hair!" exclaimed the youngest fairy.

"We have taken this magic knife by giving our hair to the water fairy magician. Now do not delay any more. Take this magical knife finish the prince and join us, said the eldest sister."

The youngest fairy took the knife and entered the cabin of the prince. The prince and his wife were sleeping . She went ahead with the knife and looked at the prince with love. She kissed his forehead and came outside. She threw the knife in the water and as she was about to jump, she was pulled up. She found herself in the sky among the clouds. Then she heard a sweet voice. "Come to us water fairy!"

"Who is it? Who is there?" asked the water fairy. She was happy to regain her ability to speak. But she again said in surprise, "Where am I? I do not understand."

"Do not be nervous. You are with the fairies. We bring the kind and good people to us. You are very sweet," said the fairies. "You have just shown your kindness to the human. She looked below at the ship of the prince and her tears fell on the ground. Fairies said, "Your tears have become dews." The water fairy went to the world of fairies in the sky.

THE AGREEMENT PAPER

Once upon a time, there lived a dog and a cat in a merchant's house. They were good friends. But the merchant was a big miser. Once he had a little loss in his business. So, he stopped giving the dog and the cat enough food to eat. They were fond of meat but they got it only once or twice in a week.

The dog and the cat used to sit together discussing things. One day, they were sitting together. "I scare the rats and save tonnes of grain," the cat said.

"I too, drive away the goats during the day and thieves during the night," the dog said.

"But our miserly master doesn't give us enough food to eat," the cat said. The next morning they went to the master and said, "Sir, if you want us to continue to serve you, you'll have to give us our salary or meat everyday."

"Salary or meat!" the master exclaimed. "What will you do with the salary? I give you food and everything."

"You don't give us meat everyday? But we do scare away rats and thieves everyday," the animals said.

"Okay I'll give you meat everyday," said the merchant.

"But we don't trust your words," the cat said. "You must sign an agreement." The merchant signed the agreement paper and give it to the animals. The cat checked it and kept it under a box in the store room.

A few days later, the merchant violated the agreement. He stopped giving meat to the animals. Both the cat and the dog were annoyed.

They went to their master and complained, "Sir, why don't you give us meat everyday? You are violating the agreement."

"What agreement?" said the merchant. "I don't remember any agreement. If you are right, then show me the paper."

"Sir, you had signed the paper yourself and now you are denying it. Isn't it a fraud? Wait, I'll show you the paper," said the cat.

The cat, at once, went to the storeroom. But, to his surprise the paper was not there! The cat only found the small bits of paper. The rats had nibbled it into tiny pieces. The cat brought some pieces and showed to the merchant. The merchant refused to accept the bits of the paper as agreement. The dog and the cat argued but the merchant didn't listen to

them.

"No agreement, no meat," said the merchant.

Now the dog was furious at the cat. He said, "You stupid cat! You have lost such an important paper. You careless creature, I'll kill you."

Saying this, the dog pounced upon the cat. The cat too ran away for his life. Then, the dog chased the cat but she fled. Since that day the dog and the cat lost friendship. The dogs run after the cats to teach them a lesson of being careless.

Similarly, the cats also chase rats because they had nibbled the agreement paper. Even today, we see a cat running after a rat and a dog running after a cat.

THE LAST OPPORTUNITY

Once upon a time there ruled a king named Vir Pratap. He was very kind and virtuous. He used to help the needy and poor people. At times, diseased persons or even those who wanted to go on pilgrimage visited the palace for financial help and the king always assisted them without any hesitation.

It was a surprising fact that the people used to come back to express their gratitude to the king once their work was complete and that their business had improved or they had recovered from their disease or that their pilgrimage was very satisfactory.

The king was very happy to know that his timely help worked and it benefitted the needy people.

But the king would get very sad whenever he thought about his own brother Vir Shakti. Vir Shakti was leading the life of a poor man. The king had expressed his desire to help him many times, but he never took the advantage of his rich brother.

Vir Shakti was an expert hunter and earned his livelihood by hunting. Besides, he was a good poet and used to recite his poems in the court. The king gave prizes to Vir Shakti for his poems and also for bringing the hunted animals. But due to his foolishness, Vir Shakti was not able to use those prizes properly. Sometimes, he lost the money bag on his way to his home or the thieves robbed him, and as a result, he remained poor like before. His apparel indicated his poverty.

One day, Vir Shakti reached the palace with many hunted animals. The king was very pleased. He decided to reward Vir Shakti and honour him in the open court. He announced his plan in the court and said, "You all know my brother Vir Shakti well. He is an expert hunter. Today, he has brought many animals which he caught in the forest. This is enough as a proof of his bravery and courage. He had put his life at risk and hunted them. His work is

worth praising. I have decided to honour him in the open court." Vir Shakti was present in the court. The king called him and gave a golden orange to him. The courtiers cheered and clapped. Vir Shakti also greeted the people and bowed before the king. Thereafter, he left the king's court for his house.

When the courtiers saw the golden orange being given to Vir Shakti, they began discussing the matter among themselves. They could not appreciate the king's decision. Rather, they were criticising the king for giving his brother only the ordinary golden orange. The king ignored the people as nobody knew that the orange consisted of valuable diamonds .

Vir Shakti also took the orange as a very ordinary fruit. However, he was satisfied that the king at least had honoured him in the open court.

Now on his way to his house, a beggar approached him for alms. Vir Shakti gave the orange to him as he had nothing else to give and said to the beggar, "You must be hungry. Take this orange to satisfy your

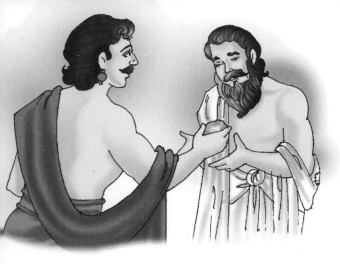

hunger."

The beggar was very happy but he was surprised to see the extraordinary orange. He decided to gift it to the king and went to the palace. Everybody was well acquainted with the kindness of the king. Hence, the guards took the beggar to the king.

The king asked the beggar to sit . The beggar took out the orange from his bag and presented to the king and said, "O king! Please accept the orange as a gift from this beggar. May God bless you a long life!"

The king accepted the orange and gave a bag full of money to the beggar. The beggar thanked the king and went away. The king recognised the orange as the one he had given to his brother Vir Shakti. He realised that his brother had again lost the opportunity of being rich. He concluded that his brother was not lucky enough to enjoy luxuries and comforts of life.

That's why he had given the orange to the beggar thinking it to be an ordinary one.

One day, the king announced a royal hunting competition and a handsome reward for the best hunter. Vir Shakti also participated in the competition. He showed his skill and won the title of the best hunter. This time again, the king gave the same orange to his brother for his success in the hunting competition.

Vir Shakti thought, 'this orange must be different from the earlier one.' So he put the orange into his bag. But when he saw a courtier with a betel leaf, he exchanged it with the orange. He was very happy to have such a tasty betel leaf and proceeded to his house.

On the other hand, the courtier went to the king and gave the orange to him saying, "Your brother has given me this orange in exchange for a betel leaf. In fact, he thought it to be useless while it is really precious. It is useless to help the people who fail to recognise its value. Such people can never be successful in

their life."

The king said nothing but announced another royal hunting competition after a fortnight. Vir Shakti again stood first in the competition.

The King announced the reward for the winner. But while giving the reward to Vir Shakti, the king said, "This is the third and the last time, that I am giving you this reward. After this, you will never be rewarded."

This time, as soon as Vir Shakti took the orange in his hand, it fell on the ground and broke into pieces. The diamonds were scattered. The king said to Vir Shakti, "Dear brother, your fate has changed. I tried to help you earlier also, but you always missed the opportunity. You gave the orange to others thinking it to be an ordinary one. But now you are rich."

This time, Vir Shakti had really become a rich man but like before he continued to help the needy and the poor.

A NEEDY PERSON

Long ago, there was a king named Brahmadutt who ruled over the state of Benaras. He loved his subjects very much. There lived a poor brahmin in a village of Benaras. He earned his livelihood by farming. He had not much agricultural land. That was why he could hardly make both ends meet. His family was suffering most. His son Somdutt was not happy as his father had to work hard in the fields from morning till evening. The Brahmin was able to earn only little cereal which was not sufficient for the survival of the family. Even their bare necessities remained unfulfilled. Somdutt realised that only agricultural earnings would not be sufficient and their poverty would never diminish. He continued to think and concluded that he must study hard and become well-educated. Only then, he would get good employment. He said to his father, "I want to study so I request you to send me to Taxila." The farmer agreed and sent his son to Taxila for studies. In

Taxila Somdutt became a pupil of a renowned teacher. After completing his education, he came back. He saw that his father was still doing hard labour to earn his livelihood. He was greatly troubled to see the suffering of his father. He decided to go to the king to get some work.

Next day, Somdutt presented himself before the king of Benaras and asked for employment. The king was very kind. He kept Somdutt in his court. But even after his getting employed, his father continued to work in the agricultural fields.

After some time, one of his ox died. Somdutt's father became very sad. Now, he was not able to plough the fields. One ox cannot pull the plough. He thought, 'Somdutt will give me some money'. So he went to his son.

On reaching Benaras, he told everything to his son. His son said, "Father, why don't you come here to live with me and leave the village. Village life is very hard." His father replied, "We have spent the whole life in our ancestral village.

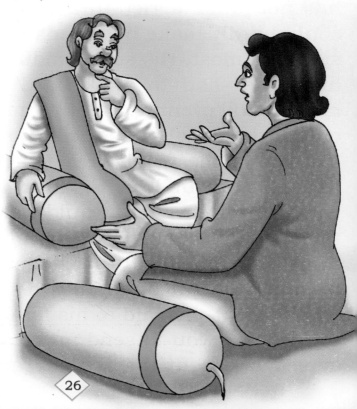

We cannot leave it and settle here. I want an ox only. So try to arrange one for me."

His son thought, 'I am a newly appointed person. How can I ask the king for money? The king will think of me as a greedy person. This is not the proper time.'

Somdutt said to his father, "If I ask the king for money or an ox, he may ask me why I need it. Besides, I do not want to misuse my official position. Hence, you should yourself tell all the problems to the king and ask for an ox. The king is very kind."

His father said, " I do not know anything except ploughing. How can I talk to the king? I am afraid of even presenting myself before him. I do not know even the way of talking to the king."

Somdutt said, " Why are you afraid of going to the king? Speak to him in the same way as you are talking to me."

But the father was still hesitating to go to the king. Somdutt wrote some words and said, "Learn these words and repeat them in front of the king." The

words were-"O king! I had two oxen, but one died. So I cannot plough my fields. Please be kind enough to give me an ox." The father mugged up these words and then went to the king with his son. As told by the son, the farmer saluted the king and stood by the side of his son. The king said, "Who are you and what do you want?" He became nervous because his son had not prepared him for this question and in confusion said, "I've come here to give you an ox." All the courtiers started laughing. Even the king laughed. The king said mockingly, "So, you have come here to give one of your ox?" The farmer said, "Yes sir." Then, he narrated everything to the king from the death of his ox, and the advice of his son. The king was very happy to learn about the behaviour and honesty of Somdutt. He thought, 'Here when everyone tries to take the advantage of his position, Somdutt is quite different . He even did not ask for help.' The king was very happy with Somdutt. He gave eight pairs of oxen to his father. The farmer returned to his village happily.

THE GREEDY MANTRIK

Long ago, there was a king named Parikshit. He was very fond of hunting. He used to spend most of his time in this activity.

One day, he went for hunting in the forest as usual. He felt thirsty so he went to the nearby ashram of the sage Shamik. But the sage was in meditation. He could not serve the king.

The king was furious and wanted to punish the sage. He saw a dead snake on a tree, picked it with the help of his sword and put it around the neck of the sage, who was still in meditation, and left.

After some time, the sage's son Shringi came there. When he saw a dead snake around the neck of his father, he enquired about it. When he came to know that it was done by the king Parikshit, he became furious. He cursed that the king that he would die on the seventh day by the bite of a snake. When the sage heard it, he became upset and told his son that he should not have cursed the king as the King was thirsty and hungry. But the curse was to have its effect. He wished that the king should be informed so that he would take steps to save his life.

When the king came to know about the curse, he got scared. He took all the steps to protect his life. He had a palace built on a hill with slippery walls and collected many anti-poisonous medicines. Besides, he asked several tantriks and mantriks to stay with him in the palace. This way, the king made all the necessary arrangements to save himself.

At last, the day of the curse came. Under the influence the of curse, Takshak was going to bite the king in the disguise of a sadhu.

On the way to the palace, Takshak met an old brahmin who was going in the same direction. Takshak asked him, "Who are you and where are you going?"

The brahmin said, "I am a mantrik brahmin. My

name is Kashyap and I am going to the king Parikshit. Today, Takshak, a serpent, will bite the king as per the curse of the sage Shringi, but I will save the king's life by my mantras. The king will give me a lot of money."

Takshak introduced himself and said, "I will use my poison on the tree and if you could revive the tree, I will believe your power of mantras." So Takshak burnt the free with his poison.

Thereafter, the Brahmin sprinkled

31

some water while chanting some mantras on the tree. The next moment, it became green again. Takshak was surprised and thought of changing the mind of the brahmin. Therefore, he said, "I accept your mantras are effective.

But just consider your decision. The king whom you want to save has no respect for the brahmins, sages, etc. He should have apologized to the sages, Shamik and Shringi, instead he has built a palace on the hill to save himself from the curse."

He continued to say, "You want to remove the effect of my poison which is backed by the curse of a great sage. The curse should not be challenged, and in case your mantras failed, it might cost you your own life. My sincere advice is that instead of challenging the curse of the sage, you should take as much money from me as you expect to receive from the king." The brahmin thought a while and agreed to take money from Takshak. He took the money and returned to his house.

Takshak entered the palace as an insect among the flowers to be presented to the king. He waited for the right opportunity and bit the king. The king died instantly.

When people came to know about the death of the king, they went to Kashyap and asked him to use his powerful mantras to save the king. Kashyap told them everything. The people cursed the brahmin saying, "You have cheated the king. When you had accepted the invitation of the king, why didn't you go there and treat him. You are greedy and ignored your duty. You will live in poverty and die in poverty."

As per the curse, the brahmin spent the rest of his life in utter poverty. The power of his mantras had already vanished.

Long ago, there lived a barber in a city with his wife. He was quite perfect in his profession. Therefore, the king appointed him as his barber. He used to come to the palace once a week to trim the hair of the king and to shave his beard. The barber was paid a good remuneration by the king which was enough for his livelihood. He worked for only one day out of the seven days of a week and spent time idly for the remaining six days. It is true, 'an empty mind is a devil's workshop'. Whenever the barber saw the courtiers wearing gold, he desired for it and said to himself, 'Why don't I have so much gold? I do not want to die in poverty.' Though the barber was not poor as he was a barber of the royal court, but he was not satisfied with whatever he had.

One day he said to his wife, "We must save money. We will purchase gold. Then you can also wear gold ornaments and walk on the road like a rich woman." His wife agreed. Both started saving money. After some time, they purchased a gold necklace and bangles. His wife wore them and felt proud.

But the barber was still not satisfied. He wanted to earn more and more money to have more gold. He only thought of gold all the time.

One day, he went to the nearby forest. When he got tired, he sat under a tree to take rest. Here also, he kept on thinking of gold and gold only. He wanted to have more and more of gold, but how? Suddenly he heard a voice coming from the tree, "Hello barber! don't be sad. Tell me what do you want. How can I help you?" The barber was surprised to hear the

sound coming from the tree. He pondered on how a tree could speak? He looked here and there but did not find anyone. He again heard the same voice coming from the tree, "O barber! you cannot see me, but I can see you. I am the soul of this tree. I have the power to fulfill the desires of people. Do not be afraid of me. Just tell me what do you want." The barber collected his courage and said, "O unknown power! I only need gold and nothing else."

The tree asked, "Are seven big pitchers of gold enough for you?" The barber said, "So much of gold! Even the king does not have this much of gold." The tree told the barber to go home and be assured that the seven big pitchers of gold would be there in his home.

The barber could not believe it. He thought he had dreamt. Anyway, he rushed home.

When he reached home, he found his wife waiting for him outside. She spoke, "Where had you been? There are seven big pitchers in the house. I do not know from where they have come. I am afraid of

36

these pitchers. I do not know what is there inside them. Do you know anything about them?" The barber was very happy and said, "Come, I will

show you what is there inside the pitchers." He uncovered all the six pitchers and found them full of gold. He jumped with joy. But when he saw the seventh pitcher, he cried, "Oh, it is cheating! This pitcher is half-filled. He became sad again.

His wife could not understand anything. She asked about the reason of his sadness. The barber told everything to his wife. She said, " We have enough gold. *Seven pitchers* of gold are more than enough. It makes no difference whether the seventh pitcher is half-filled. We will fill it with our labour. Do not be sad." The barber agreed and said, "I want to see the seventh pitcher filled with gold at any cost." Now both started working hard to earn a lot. They started saving money by all means including fasting and eating less food. Consequently, they became very weak. They were trying to fill the seventh pitcher but it did not fill up even after a long time.

One day, the king asked the barber why he was becoming weak day by day; was he suffering from any disease. The barber told the king that he was very worried about money. The king said, "Oh! It is not a big problem. I will double the payment made to you." He ordered the cashier accordingly.

But this help of the king was not sufficient. The pitcher was still not full. The barber and his wife continued to save money by taking less food. But the pitcher remained as it was i.e. half–filled.

Seeing the barber's deteriorating heath, the king said to the barber, " Tell me the truth. I think you must have got seven gold pitchers from a tree of the forest." The barber was surprised to hear the king. He asked him, "How did you come to know this?"

The king said, "Once I also got those pitchers in the forest. I accepted the pitchers, but the seventh one was half-filled. Out of greed, I tried my best to fill the pitcher, but still it remained the same. I lost my health as

well." The barber asked eagerly, "What did you do then?" The king said, "I realised that greed is an evil and it has no end, and the tree wanted to teach this lesson to me. I eventually went to the tree and requested him to take all the pitchers back. I returned to my palace and saw that pitchers were not there. Since then I am happy and have enough money."

Then barber also disclosed the truth of having seven pitchers. The king warned him, "Still there is no harm done. It would be better to return all the pitchers immediately. Otherwise nobody will be able to save you." The barber pondered for a while and decided to handover the pitchers to the tree. Hence,

 he went to the forest and requested the tree to take the pitchers back and then came back home. There, he found no pitcher. Since then the couple realised that greed is one of the deadly sins and a greedy person cannot live peacefully.

HOW MAN GOT FIRE

Once upon a time there lived a ferocious devil named Tumba in a cave near the Rotma mountain of Fiji. He could produce fire from his mouth. The heat of the fire could burn anything to ashes. But fortunately, he preferred to sleep all the time like Kumbhakarna. Whenever, he came out of his cave, even his slight yawning and breathing would cause the leaves and plants to burn.

There was a village in the valley of the mountain. The villagers were very much afraid of Tumba. They always prayed to God to make the devil sleep all the time. They also wished that the devil should remain confined to the cave only.

There were four brave youths in the same village. They were not at all afraid of the devil. Actually, they wanted to catch the fire of the devil's mouth.

One day, one of them said, "If we knew how to produce fire, we would eat cooked food and not the raw stuff."

Another youth said, "Fire also produces light and removes darkness."

The third friend said, "Now we must steal the fire from the mouth of the devil."

The fourth friend said, "Let us go to steal the fire."

All the four were now ready to go to the Rotma mountain. They were not afraid of the devil. They collected dry leaves of the coconut and proceeded to the mountain stealthily. Soon, they reached the cave of the devil. They waited outside the cave for the right time so that they could enter the cave without the knowledge of the devil. When they entered the cave furtively, Tumba was sleeping soundly. Even in his sleep, he was discharging hot waves of fire. They went near the devil and put the dry leaves of the coconut near his mouth. The leaves caught the fire. The youths were overexcited and ran with the burning leaves towards the village. Meanwhile, the devil woke up and ran after the youths shouting at the top of his voice, "How dare you steal the fire from my mouth!" The youths ran even faster. Soon, they reached another cave, quickly entered and closed its mouth with a heavy stone. Now they were safe and talked to each other about their adventure. One of them said, "Thank God, we have successfully closed the mouth of the cave." Another one said, "But we can not live here forever, we will have to get out of this trouble."

Following them, the devil also reached there. He got furious to see that the mouth of the cave was closed with a heavy stone. He roared outside the cave and produced fire which made the inside hot.

The four youths in the cave were unable to tolerate the heat of the fire. They were upset and were thinking how to get rid of the devil.

On the other side, Tumba wanted to kill them by hook or crook. He cunningly said, "Oh dear friends, if you allow me to enter the cave, I will sing a song for you which would be really enjoyable."

The youths shifted the stone a bit. Seeing this, the devil said, "How can I enter through this little space. Make it a bit wide and allow me to come into the cave."

At this stage, one of the youths thought of a plan to kill the devil. He whispered his plan to other friends. They all agreed to follow. They were sure of their success. Accordingly, they shifted the stone a little

more to enable the devil to enter the cave. As soon as the devil pushed his head inside, the youths closed the door with the stone again and this way they crushed his head. Consequently, the teeth of the devil broke and fell on the ground. He had lost his breath. Now seeing the devil dead, all the youths ran towards the village shouting at the top of their voice, "We have killed the devil! Now his teeth would never produce fire. We have brought the fire with us as well."

And they distributed the fire among all the villagers. Thus, they got fire to cook food and produce light. All the villagers thanked the youths and honoured them.

THE STORY OF PATLIPUTRA

Long ago, there lived a brahmin in a village near Benaras. He had three sons. When his sons grew older, he sent them to Magadh for studies. After the completion of their studies they came back to their village. But their father died after some days.

After the death of their father, they all decided to go on a pilgrimage to the southern part of the country. With this view, they set out on their journey.

The three brothers reached an old city named Ramnathpuram on the shore of the sea. They were tired so they approached a learned man called Pandit Rameshwar who accepted them as his guests.

By chance, Panditji had three young daughters. Panditji thought, 'These boys are brahmins and are well-educated. It will be good to marry my daughters to them.' He materlised this idea. After their marriage, he distributed his property among them

equally and went for the pilgrimage, never to return.

The days passed smoothly until there was famine in the area. The three brothers faced the problem for quite some time. But when the situation became worse, they ran away leaving their wives behind.

The three sisters were in trouble now. The second sister was pregnant. So they took shelter in the house of Indradutt, who was a friend of their father. He was very intelligent, kind and treated them as his own daughters. When the time came, the sister gave birth to a boy. All the three sisters loved the child very much, and looked after him well. Seeing the great affection of the three sisters for the child, Lord Shiva appeared in their dreams and said, "The name of the child would be Putrak. There would be one lakh gold coins under his bed, and he would grow up

to be a king." The words of Shiva in the dreams proved to be true. When they woke up they found one lakh gold coins under his bed. It was repeated daily and a huge wealth got collected soon and the child became a king.

One day, Indradutt said to Putrak, "Charity is a great thing. If you start donating to brahmins, it is possible that your father and uncles who left before your birth may return."

On the advice of Indradutt, Putrak began to donate to the brahmins. When his father and his uncles heard about the prosperity of Putrak, they came to live in the palace. But they were very cunning by nature. They thought of taking over the kingdom by killing Putrak. As per their plan, they went to a temple at the Vindhya along with Putrak. There they had hired some men to kill him.

When the men came to kill him, Putrak asked them the reason. They disclosed

that his father and uncles had hired them to kill him so that they could get your kingdom. Putrak said, "I will give you even more money. Just leave me here and do not tell this secret to anyone." The men agreed. They lied to his father that they had killed him. When the three brahmins returned to the kingdom without Putrak, the courtiers and the ministers realised that they must have killed the king. So they were also killed by them.

On the other hand, Putrak proceeded to Vindhyachal mountain. He met two chandals who were fighting for the possession of a pair of wooden sandal, one pot and a stick. According to them, one could fly on wearing the sandals, the pot could supply anything and the stick could write.

Putrak thought, 'These magical things may help me. So he said, "Do not quarrel over these things. I suggest you both to run a race, and whoever wins, would get these things."

Following the advice both the chandals ran to win the race, leaving the magical things behind. Getting this opportunity, Putrak and picked the things wore the wooden sandals to fly into the sky. He

saw a city below and got down. He met an old lady, paid some money and made arrangement to stay with her. He behaved well and soon the old lady began to treat him as her own son. This way, Putrak lived there in hiding.

After some time, the old lady encouraged Putrak to get married and said, " You are like my son and hence, I am worried about your marriage." She also suggested that the princess of this state was suitable for him. Putrak said, "Mother! You need not worry at all. I will marry the princess. I will meet her today."

At night, Putrak reached the room of the princess with the help of his magic sandals. At first the princess Patli was afraid, but soon, she fell in love with him. Both talked and enjoyed each other's company. Thereafter, Putrak went back to his house with a

promise to come again. They continued to meet daily. When the king came to know about the affair, he wanted to get Putrak arrested. But Putrak flew away taking the princess with him. They flew high in the sky and crossed the state. Thereafter, they got down at a beautiful place along the bank of the Ganga. They prepared food with the help of the magical pot and discussed about their future. The princess said, "The place is very beautiful. I have never seen such a beauty. I wish to live here for ever."

Putrak also said, " You are right. I have never seen such a beautiful place before."

He further said, "Now let us live here. I will draw a picture of our dream city.

So Putrak took out his magical stick and drew a beautiful city with a fort, palace, market, etc. He extended his kingdom later in his life.

INSANITY

Once a rich businessman lived in a city. He knew the value of money and that was why he never spent money on useless things. He had only one son. He directed his son not to waste money. But his son did not like his advices and was fond of spending money on luxurious items. He also liked to enjoy the company of friends.

One day the businessman died of a heart attack. His son inherited all his father's wealth, and started spending lavishly on his friends. Soon, all his money finished.

Despite that, he failed to mend his habits and continued to live in the same style. Now he started borrowing money from moneylenders. His friends praised him in his presence but laughed at his follies behind his back.

Time passed smoothly until the moneylenders started demanding their money back and also filed a

suit in the court. The youth thought of acting mad in the court to save himself from punishment. The court declared him a mad person and recommended him to send to an asylum. There he was examined by the doctors, who declared his disease incurable. While in the hospital, the youth was becoming mentally disturbed due to the regular practice of madness.

One day, one of his friends came to meet him who knew that his friend was acting to avoid punishment for non-payment of loans. He realised that his friend was really becoming mad. So he warned his friend, "Stop acting as a mad man. Otherwise you will become the same in reality, and in that case, you will have to live in the mental hospital throughout your life."

So the youth became cautious. He realised that he himself was ruining his life. He stopped posing as a mad person. He came out of the hospital and promised all the moneylenders to pay back their debts in time. He joined a firm and worked day and night. He returned the loan soon and lived happily

Long ago, there lived a poor farmer named Sunderlal in a village of Champaran. A moneylender named Sukhram also lived in the same village. The moneylender had amassed huge wealth by cheating the innocent farmers. The people knew about the dishonesty of Sukhram, but they had no other way to get money. Whenever they needed they had to go to Sukhram.

Before giving money to anyone, Sukhram used to make the loan seeker mortgage his property such as house, animals or agricultural land by getting his signatures on the document. In case the debtor failed to return the loan amount, he used to forfeit the mortgaged property.

Sunder was also under the debt of Sukhram. He was unable to pay back the loan. Therefore, the moneylender took the possession of everything which belonged to Sunder–his fields, crops, house, etc.

One day, Sukhram went to Sunderlal for the recovery of the loan, who told him, "I have nothing except the clothes on my body. I am unable to return your loan."

Hearing it, Sukhram said, " Why don't you go to Ram who always help me. He will certainly help you too." Saying this he went away.

Sunder thought, 'I would certainly go in search of Ram. If he has helped Sukhram, he will certainly help me too.' So he went in search of Ram. On his way, he met a saint. He said to the him, "Baba! I am searching for Ram for many days. Can you help me in finding the whereabouts of Ram? I will give you a piece of bread in exchange, if you guide me to find Ram."

The saint did not pay any heed to the request of Sunderlal and went away. He kept his search on. After covering some distance, he met another saint

with a sacred mark of ashes on his forehead. He said to him, " Baba! please help me in my search for Ram. I can give a piece of bread to you." The saint took the bread and said, "I know Shiva and not Ram," And he went away. Sunderlal continued his search

for Ram. He became tired and felt hungry. But he did not lose courage. Sometime later, he saw a poor man coming towards him. There was a similarity in their conditions. Sunderlal said to that poor man, " Hello friend! I have been searching for Ram for many days. I want his help to overcome my acute poverty. Would you take me to Ram. I will give you all the pieces of bread that I have." Sunderlal opened his packet of bread.

The poor man said, "Oh! you are looking for Ram. I can take you to him. Actually, I am Ram. Tell me what I can do for you."

Then both of them started eating the bread. Sunderlal narrated the story of his ruin—how the moneylender had cheated him.

Hearing his account the poor man took out a *Shankh* (conch) from his bag and said to Sunderlal, "Take it. All your problems will be solved by this conch. Blow it with special tune and it will respond as per your wishes. I am weak and hence, I want you to keep it in safe custody." So he taught a typical tune to him and left.

Sunderlal returned to his house and in a closed room blew the conch. As the old man had said gold coins dropped from its other side. He became very happy on getting the gold coins. He purchased the necessary things for himself. He also bought some seeds and sowed in the small barren field left with him. Since then he went to his field daily and looked after his crop well. As a result his field had a good crop.

One day, the moneylender happened to pass by the field of Sunderlal. He was surprised to see abundant crop in his fields. He went to Sunderlal and congratulated him, and said, " I have not come to ask you for the money, but tell me how this miracle happened."

The innocent Sunderlal was unable to understand the cleverness of Sukhram. He disclosed everything to the moneylender and showed him the conch.

Seeing the magical conch, Sukhram now wanted to have it. While leaving the house he stole the conch and hid it in his pocket.

That day, Sunderlal remained busy in his work and did not think about the conch even for once. He had faith in Ram who had helped him in gaining prosperity.

On the other hand having reached home, Sukhram tried to blow the conch. But he could not blow it despite all his efforts. He decided to return the conch to Sunderlal.

Next day, he went to Sunderlal and returned the conch to him saying, "I am sorry to take the conch at home. Actually, I wanted to test it but I could not blow it. Can you just show me how it works?"

The innocent Sunderlal could not understand the intentions of Sukhram even then. As he blew the conch, gold coins fell on the ground. The moneylender thought of another plan to cheat Sunderlal. He said to him, " I waive all the debts given to you on the condition that whatever money you get on blowing the conch, I get just the double of that amount."

Hearing it, Sunderlal became very sad and said

to the moneylender, "Till now you have cheated me and have grabbed my land, house and other things. Before I accept your condition, you have to return all that you have taken from me." The moneylender thought for a moment and said, "In that condition, the conch shall remain with me," and he took the possession of the conch. As he was about to go, Sunderlal said, "I accept your condition. Return my conch to me." He further said, "One thing more, you shall also return my utensils and make my land free from mortgage."

Sukhram was upset but he was expecting huge money from the conch. As such, he accepted the condition and returned the utensils. He also made the land of Sunderlal free from mortgage.

When Sunderlal got everything back, he thought of taking revenge from the moneylender. He blew the conch with the desire of his losing one eye. This in turn made the moneylender completely blind as he had wished to get the double of whatever Sunderlal got. This way a simple man took his revenge in a different way.

GOOD AND BAD

Once upon a time there was a king named Vinaysheel. He had several queens. When he became old, his young queens started ignoring him. The king was not pleased at such a behaviour of the queens. He ordered his royal physician to prepare a medicine that can make him young again.

Knowing the desire of the king, the physician was surprised. He thought, 'What a big fool the king is! He knows well that old age is unavoidable and a human being cannot become young again.' He continued to think, 'I must take advantage of the situation. The king can be cheated easily and a lot of money can be extracted from him by giving excuses.'

Having decided so, he approached the king and said, "O king. It is not a difficult work for me. But you have to follow my instructions strictly during the course of treatment."

The king agreed to this and said, "I will follow all your instructions in order to become young again." Then, the physician said, "Maharaj, my medicine will not work in the sunlight and hence, you will have to live in the underground cell where no sunlight can reach."

So the king said, "All right, I will get the cell prepared. Go and make the medicine at once."

The physician further made the conditions clear and said, "You will have to live alone in the cell. Nobody will be allowed to enter it. The food and water will be kept near the door of the cell."

"All right," said the king.

The king ordered his men to make an underground cell immediately. Soon it was ready. Now the physician became very happy and thought, 'The king will die soon in the cell and I will manage the kingdom.'

The physician thus sent the king into the cell and started pretending as if he was treating the king. He consoled the king on one hand and was conspirating against him on the other hand to remove him from the throne.

The physician asked his men to dig a tunnel from the

forest to the cell. Thereafter, he started searching for a man who resembled the king.

One day, he saw a man on the bank of the river who quite resembled the king. The physician went to him and said, "It appears that you have come to this city for the first time."

The youth replied, "Yes you are right, but why do you enquire about me?"

The physician said, "The matter is profitable for you. Take me as your friend and do as I tell. I will make you the king of this city."

The youth was surprised and said, "I understand you. Who are you and why do you want to make me the king?"

The royal physician said, "My name is Tarunchand and I am the royal physician of this state. The king is under my control."

The youth said, "Tell me what will I have to do to become the king."

The physician said, "You will just have to stay in an underground cell for a few days."

The youth said, "All right," then gave his address to the physician and went away.

The physician quickly made out a plan to kill the king and mixed poison in the drink and gave it to the king. When the king drank the wine, he fell down on the ground. The physician carried the dead body of the king through the tunnel and threw it into a well in the forest. Thereafter, he brought the youth to the cell through the tunnel. He said to the youth, "You will have to live in this cell till your beard and moustache grow enough to cover your face. Then I will take you to the palace. You are supposed to behave as if you have recovered from the old age and have become young again."

The youth expressed his doubt what if someone recognised him, how would he deal with the situation. The physician said, "Don't worry. I am

with you." After a few days, he announced in the royal court that his medicine had made the king young once again and he would be coming to the palace the next day. He further said, "We should be ready to welcome the king."

Hearing the news of the king becoming young again, the courtiers and the queens were extremely happy.

Next day, the physician presented the young king in the palace and told him to occupy the throne.

All were impressed to see the new appearance of the king. The physician then advised the king to rename himself. The king said, "Why don't you suggest a name?"

The physician said that the name 'Ajar' would be most appropriate for him. The king accepted the new name and all the courtiers cheered .

The new king followed the instructions of the physician in the beginning, but started ignoring his advices later. The physician said to him, "You have changed a lot. I think you have forgotten your promise."

The king said, "What promise? I do not remember any promise."

The physician then reminded him, "The promise that you would run the state affairs just as I would tell you."

The king said, "You are a physician and not a minister. I have to run the state affairs with the help of my ministers."

The physician got annoyed and said, "You should be obliged to me for the royal life that I have given you."

The king said, "No, you have not made me the king. It is all due to my good deeds of the previous birth."

The physician said, "Can you prove this to me?"

The King advised him to wait for the right time. The physician expressed his resentment and went away.

One day, the king went out for a walk along the bank of the river with some of his ministers

and the physician as well. He saw some beautiful lotus flowers floating in the river and said, "I have never seen such beautiful flowers before."

The ministers agreed and said, "These lotus flowers will enhance the beauty of the royal pond in the palace."

The king agreed to the suggestion of the ministers and said to the physician, "You have a good knowledge of vegetation. Try to find out the origin of these flowers by following it along the river. And, if possible, bring some seeds of these flowers, so that these can be sowed in the royal pond."

The physician could not say 'No' to the king. He reached the origin of the river by going upstream. There he saw a temple of Lord Shiva and a skeleton hanging upside down on a big banyan tree.

The physician went near the skeleton and thought, 'Whose skeleton is this? Why is it hanging upside

down? What is the mystery behind it?'

The physician kept on thinking. Suddenly the weather changed and it began to rain heavily. The physician took shelter under the banyan tree. He was surprised to see that the drops of rain that touched the skeleton turned into lotus flowers before falling into the river. After some time, when the rain stopped, he tried to take the skeleton off the banyan tree. But the skeleton slipped and fell into the river. Then the physician returned to the king and told him every thing. At this, the king said, "The skeleton you saw was of my previous birth. I was a yogi and did a severe penance, hanging upside down from the tree to please Lord Shiva. During this meditation, I died and my hanging body turned into a skeleton. Thank god! It is fully disposed now."

The physician said, "That is all right but it did not help me to make you the king. You have forgotten my obligations and have ignored me."

The king said, "I am a king due to the good deeds of my previous birth. Everyone gets a reward or punishment as per their deeds. You will also be punished for your wrong deeds. Remember it."

The physician came back to his house. One day, he went to the forest in search of some medicinal plants. He reached the same well in which he had thrown the dead body of the king Vinaysheel. There were beautiful flowers around the well. He could not resist himself from going closer to the well to get the flowers. As he tried to pluck them, he slipped and fell down into the well. He cried for help but none came. He died there. Thus, he got his punishment.

A BENEVOLENT MONKEY

There was a beautiful place in the foothills of the Himalayas. Nature had spread its beauty all around in the form of trees, rivers and spring. The valleys of beautiful flowers further added to its beauty.

A monkey by the name of Daya lived in this green area. He was a saint by nature as he possessed all the good habits. He loved and was very kind to all. He also used to help others in their troubles.

One day a person came there in search of his cow. He was tired and almost exhausted. He sat under a tree to take rest. He was feeling hungry. He looked here and there for something to eat. The monkey thought of the man as his guest and to keep him hungry would be sinful. So he brought some plums and kept near the tree where he was lying. He, then dropped a fruit to attract his attention which he heard and was pleased to see some plums lying near him. He ate

and found them to be very tasty. When he looked up for more but found that it was not the plum tree. He searched and soon found it near a hill. He climbed up the tree to pluck its fruit. Its delicate branches already loaded with fruit could not bear the weight of the person. It broke and he fell in the deep *trench* below.

It was very difficult for the man to come out of the trench as it was very deep. He could not gather courage to climb up on the slippery mountain. Many days passed by. He survived on the plums that were lying there along with the broken branch. But the condition of the person was worsening day by day.

One day, the kind monkey Daya happened to pass by that place. He was feeling hungry. He went near the plum tree. He was surprised to see the man lying in the deep trench. Although the monkey wanted to satisfy his hunger, yet seeing the man in distress, he preferred to help him first. He stopped climbing the tree and got down to help the man. Forgetting his hunger, he approached the person and comforted him, "Hello! Now I am here. You need not worry at all. Wait a little more. I will definitely take you out of this trench."

Thereafter, he rehearsed with a stone equal to the weight of the man by taking it on his back out of the trench. When he felt that he could take the man out, he said, "Do not lose heart. Sit on my back, I am going to take you out soon."

He further said to the man, "Now, listen to me attentively. While I am ascending the hill, hold me firmly. As soon as you see that I am out of the trench and there is no danger to you, jump from my body to relieve me from the load."

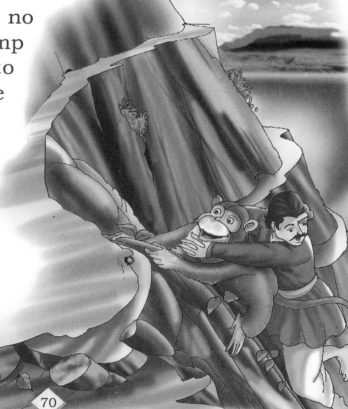

The man sat on the back of the monkey and caught him tightly. After some time, both of them came out of the trench. It was a tough exercise for the monkey. He was totally exhausted and tired. He lay down on the ground and said to the man, "The forest is full of wild animals. I am going to sleep for a while to recover from the fatigue. Take care of me as well as of yourself." So Daya went off to sleep on a nearby rock. The man assured Daya saying, "Friend! Take a sound sleep. I will keep a watch all around."

After the monkey slept, the man thought otherwise. He had become weak as he had nothing much to eat during his fall in the trench. For a fast recovery, he thought of eating the monkey. So he picked up a large stone and aimed it on the head of the monkey. As the man was weak, the stone slipped and fell some distance away from the animal, creating a big sound.

Hearing the loud sound, the monkey woke and realised the bad intention of the man. He was

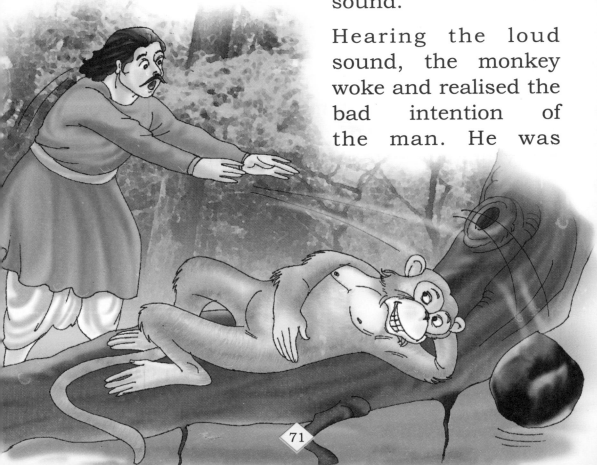

surprised by this and asked him, "You had assured to keep a watch but instead you wanted to kill me, Why?"

The man had nothing to say, so he kept silent.

Daya felt pity on him and said, "Friend! although I am a monkey, yet I saved your life. But you, a human behaved in an ungrateful manner. I am really hurt."

Daya further said to him, "Now, let me lead you out of this dense forest . I do not want you to lose your life by falling prey to some wild animal."

!Thereafter, the monkey helped the man out of the forest and said, "Friend! Now you are out of danger. You can go to your house without any worries. May God help you!"

!The good-natured monkey returned to the forest and lived in peace. But the guilty man could never live in peace. He led a life full of misery and sorrow.

A CLEVER CHILD

Once there was a brahmin named Rudradutt. He had two wives. Unfortunately one of the wives died while delivering a baby. But the baby was safe. The younger wife was given the responsibility of bringing up the baby.

The baby grew up slowly because his stepmother never gave sufficient food and hardly even took care of him. Thus, the child became very weak. Rudradutt was worried. Once he asked his wife, "Why don't you feed the boy properly?"

His wife replied, "This allegation is wrong. I love and treat the boy like my own son. I do not know what has happened to him."

The Brahmin loved her very much, so he trusted her words.

Since the boy was being ignored, he felt weak and preferred to remain at home all the time. His childhood was spoiled. People began calling him 'dull head.'

After some time, a son was born to the younger wife. She loved her child very much. The elder son observed it and was deeply hurt by her behaviour. He decided to take revenge on his stepmother even at the tender age of 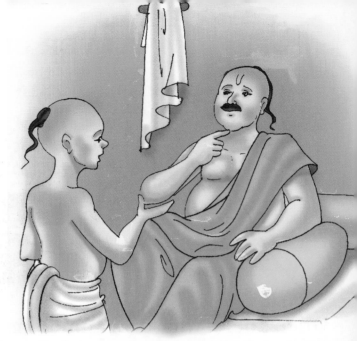 five. One day when his father came back from work, he said, "I have two fathers."

The brahmin suspected his wife of loose character and stopped talking to her. The wife felt distressed and tried to find out the reason of her husband's changed behaviour but all in vain. She realised that her stepson must have said something against her.

One day, she fed her stepchild with delicious food and patted him with great love and affection. Then she asked, "What did you say to your father? Your father's behaviour is changed."

The child said, "It is just a beginning. Wait and see my further actions against you."

The mother said, "You are my son. You should not go against me. I will treat you well."

The son said, "You do not love and treat me well. Why should I think of you? You give me stale food."

His stepmother now realised that she should take care of her stepson and tried to pacify him. Further, she said to her stepson, "I promise that from now onwards, I will make no discrimination between my two sons. And you will have nothing to

complain in future. I only wish that you do not talk against me and try to convince your father in my favour."

The child promised to do so. He asked his mother to show the mirror to the father when he would come home in the evening.

So when Rudradutt came home, his wife showed a mirror to him. At this very moment, the child came there and pointed to his father's reflection said, "This is my second father."

The brahmin realised his mistake and felt sorry for suspecting his wife and misbehaving with her. He became normal and began to love her as before.

Long ago there lived a trader named Ali in Sind. He used to go from one city to another for trade purposes.

Once he went to a city for his business. There he stayed in an inn. During the day, he earned a lot of money in the business. He was very happy. By the evening, he was tired of his daylong roaming. Hence, he decided to take rest under a tree.

There lived two swindlers in that city. When they saw Ali relaxing under a tree, they thought of a plan to cheat him. They approached Ali and said , "We know you are here for the business. We can help you. We are the best guides in the city. You can earn a lot with our help."

Ali replied, "Yes! you can come with me. I am tired and would like to take some rest. You both can stay in the next room at the inn." So they accompanied him.

On reaching there, Ali requested the owner to give the room next to him to his new friends. The

innkeeper accepted his request and allotted the desired room to Ali's friends. They all went to their respective rooms to sleep.

In their room, both the thugs discussed a plan and decided to kill Ali during the evening walk and take all his belongings. One of them said excitedly, "This way, we will become rich overnight."

Next day, Ali earned a bit more by their help. In the evening, both asked Ali to have a walk with them. "After evening walk we will take dinner together." But Ali refused and said, "I am not hungry, you may go."

Both the thugs went to different directions for food. They were not faithful to each other. Each one wanted to kill the other. Neither of them wanted to share the booty, after Ali was killed. On the way they planned to kill each other and mixed poison in the food.

When they returned from the market, one of them asked the other, "What is there in your dinner?" The other one replied, "Curry and bread." "Oh! I have also bought the same food items. Let us exchange our meals for a better friendship," replied the first.

Since each one wanted to kill the other, they agreed to exchange their poisoned meal. Each of them was

very happy thinking that the other one would die of poison and he will get all the booty. But they did not know that both had mixed poison in the food and they both would die.

After they ate the dinner, they went to sleep. At midnight they started vomiting and felt suffocated. By the end of the night, they both were lying dead.

In the morning, while the owner of the inn was taking a round, he was surprised to see them dead. He informed Ali. Other people also assembled there. They understood what had happened. One of them said, "These people used to fool others to loot their money." Ali said, "They both wanted to cheat me also but they cheated each other by mixing poison in each other's food." The owner of the inn said, " God has punished them for their misdeeds."

JATIN

Once there lived a child named Jatin with his mother in a village. His father died early when he was very small. His mother used to work in other people's houses as a maid to earn a livelihood. His mother was a devotee of Lord Krishna and worshipped him both in the morning and evening. When Jatin grew up, his mother sent him to a school in a nearby village as there was no school in her own village. There was a forest on the way to the other village. The first day, his mother accompanied him to the school to tell him the route. Next day, she said to him, "I have shown you the way, now you should go to the school alone. I have to go to work. You are an intelligent boy, go to the school cautiously and carefully." Jatin knew his mother cannot go with him daily. If she accompany him everyday to the

school there will be no earnings and no bread even. He said, "I can go alone. Do not worry about me." He picked up his bag and left for the school. On his way, he was afraid of the wild animals and reached school with difficulty. On

the way back, he had to cross the forest again. He got frightened while he was passing through the bushes. He rushed to reach home as quickly as possible. As soon as he reached home, he fell on the floor and started weeping bitterly. His mother was very upset and tried to console her son, "Jatin! why are you crying? Tell me, what happened to you? Has someone beaten you or your teacher scolded you?" Jatin sobbed and said, "No mother, nobody did anything to me. I am afraid of the wild animals in the forest. They will kill and eat me. I will not go to school alone." And, he hugged his mother.

His mother prayed to Lord Krishna in the evening, "Oh Gopal! I cannot go to school with my son daily. There is no one except me to accompany him to the school. Please show me the way." When she finished her pooja (worship), she looked assured and her face was shining with happiness.

At dinner, she said to Jatin, "I forgot to tell you that there is an elder brother of yours. He will accompany you to the school."

Jatin was surprised to know it and said, "You have never told me about my elder brother. Why doesn't he live with us?"

His mother said, "He lives in the forest and take cows for grazing." Jatin said, "Yes mother, will you tell him to accompany me in the forest?" The mother said, "Yes my son, you need not worry now. Whenever you will call him, he will be there with you." Then Jatin asked, "What is the name of my brother?" The mother replied, "His name is Madhusudan. He is very nice. He always helps others."

Next day, when Jatin became ready for school, he said to his mother, "Now I need not fear as my brother is there."

He went to school happily. But as he reached near the forest, he trembled with fear of wild animals. He called his brother, "Brother Madhusudan! please come immediately. Help me in crossing the forest. I am afraid of the wild

animals. Please come fast." But nobody came there. He again called for help, but all in vain. He started weeping and said, "Madhusudan, mother told me that you would come to help me whenever I need you. Now I am all alone in the forest, but you are not coming."

At this moment he heard the sound of the flute. He looked here and there but found none. Soon he saw a handsome boy wearing a crown of peacock feathers.

Jatin ran to the boy, clutched his hand and said, "It is good that you have come. Now no wild animals will kill me. I know you are Madhusudan. But why didn't you come on my first call?"

He said, "Yes, I am Madhusudan. I have come here to help you. Now you need not fear any more. Come, I will take you across the forest."

They both crossed the forest. Jatin told him about

the school, teachers and friends. After crossing the forest, Madhusudan said to Jatin, "Go to school, now I have to return to my cows. When you need me, call me again."

Since then, Jatin went to the school and also came back home alone. He always felt the presence of his brother and his fear vanished.

This way, few months passed, one day, his teacher said in the class, "Children! There will be summer vacation soon. Before it, we are going to arrange a party and we will eat together. This party will be held tomorrow. Every student is expected to bring some food from his house."

On reaching home, Jatin told his mother about the feast in the school. His mother became sad. She said to Jatin, "Had you told me a day before, I would have collected some food for you. But it is not possible now." Jatin became sad. But next moment, his face shone

with joy. He said to his mother, "My brother has so many cows. He must have curd and butter. I will ask him to bring some curd for me." His mother said, "Yes, you are right. I am sure he will help you." Next day, on his way to school, Jatin called his brother. When Madhusudan appeared, Jatin asked him to arrange curd for his classmates as his mother had no food at home.

Madhusudan smiled and said to Jatin, "Wait here for a while, I will bring curd for you." As he turned to go, Jatin said, "Listen, there are twenty classmates. So bring sufficient curd for all of them."

Madhusudan stopped, looked behind and then disappeared in the forest.

After some time, he came back with a pitcher of curd and said, "Here is fresh curd for you. Take it and distribute it among your class-mates."

Jatin was very happy. He took the pitcher of curd. But it was very small. Hence, Jatin thought whether the curd would be sufficient for the whole class or not. But he did not say anything to

Madhusudan. He went to the school with the pitcher of curd. Seeing a small pot of curd, his teacher became angry and scolded Jatin, "You have brought a small pot of curd, which will not be sufficient for the whole class. If other children had done the same thing, the whole class would be hungry."

All the children enjoyed the party except Jatin. When all the children finished the feast, the teacher asked Jatin to distribute the curd in the class.

Jatin started distributing the curd among the classmates. To his surprise, the small pot of curd continued to fill again and again. The curd did not finish even after its liberal distribution. The curd was very tasty. His teacher was also surprised to see that small pot contained so much. He asked Jatin, "From where did you bring the pot of curd?" He answered, "My elder brother had given me the curd." The teacher said, "You never told about your brother

before." Jatin said, "He lives in the forest and hardly comes home. He graze the cows in the forest." The teacher wished to meet his brother and asked him, "Can I go with you to the forest?"

Jatin said, "Why not? You may come with me."

After the school, the teacher accompanied Jatin to the forest. On reaching there, Jatin called his brother, but there was no response. Jatin repeated his call, but all in vain. At this, his teacher got angry and said, "Jatin, you are a big liar! Where is your brother?" Jatin started crying and said, "I am not telling a lie." He then cried, "Brother, why don't you come? My teacher is calling me a liar." Right than, he heard the sound of the flute. His teacher also heard the music. Then Jatin heard a whispering sound in his ear, "Listen! you can see me but your teacher will not be able to see as he has no faith in me. You continue to have faith in me and I will always help you." Jatin realised that his brother was none other than Lord Krishna who protected him in all his troubles.

TOM THUMB

Once there lived a couple who were cultivators. They did not have any child and hence, they were very sad. One day, the cultivator's wife prayed to God, "Oh God! if you bless me with a little child, even if he is as small as a thumb, I would be happy. I will bring him up with great love and affection."

God heard her prayer. Soon a son was born to her who was as short as a thumb. The couple's joy knew no bounds. They named him Tom Thumb. With the passage of time, he grew older, but his height was still the same. However, he grew to be very intelligent and wise.

One day, he went to the forest with his father. His father cut the wood and loaded his horse cart. Tom Thumb asked his father to allow him to lead the cart to the house. His father permitted and he himself went home through a shorter route. Tom Thumb sat in one of the ears of the horse and guided the cart. He was not visible to others. The cart was without a driver. It surprised all. When the cart was passing through a village, two strangers followed it. They did not know about the presence of Tom Thumb in the ear of the horse. When the cart reached home, Tom Thumb said loudly, "Father, I have reached home. Help me in getting down from the cart." Both the strangers were surprised to hear the voice. They observed that a man was helping a boy who was as big as a thumb to come out. They had never seen such a small person in their lives. They thought of purchasing the boy for their use and approached the father of Tom Thumb, "We want to purchase this boy. And we are ready to pay any amount you wish."

But the father was not ready to sell his son and said, "I can not accept your offer. I will not give my son to anyone for any price."

But Tom Thumb tried to convince his father, "Do not worry about me. I will come back home. Take the money from these people and sell me to them."

His father finally agreed after much persuasion and then handed over Tom Thumb to them.

Tom Thumb accompanied the strangers. They stopped at an inn during the night.

They put Tom on the ground and were engaged in gossips. There was a hole of a rat nearby. Tom entered the hole to hide from the two men.

There he saw the shell of a snail. He quickly entered the shell and heard their conversation. They were planning to commit theft in the house of a priest. Tom came out of the shell and said, "Take me with you. I will be of great help to you."

Both agreed and allowed Tom to join them. Then all of them went to the house of the priest.

Here, Tom Thumb cried, "Whatever you want, you will get here. You can take all." The men told Tom to keep quiet. But Tom ignored their warning and continued to shout with an intention of waking up the people of the house. The maid of the priest got up on hearing the

noise and shouted, "Who is there? Who is there?" Tom had ruined their plan. They had no other way but to run away. And Tom hid himself in the stable. The maid lit a candle and finding no one, went to bed again. She thought, 'It must have been a dream.' Tom spent the night in the stable. He slept on the grass meant for the cow to eat.

Next day, when the maid gave the grass to the cow, Tom was eaten up by it. When the maid went to the cow again, Tom cried from the cow's stomach, "Do not serve the grass any more." The maid got afraid of the cow and ran to the priest. But the priest did not believe. He himself came to verify the maid's statement. When he reached the stable, he himself heard the cow speaking like a human being. Now the priest decided to kill the cow and asked his servants to perform the task. They left the cow in the forest where a wolf killed and ate the cow. Tom was now

inside the belly of the wolf. Tom still did not lose hope. He spoke to the wolf, "My dear wolf, I know you wish for a good food. I know the place where good and tasty food is available."

The wolf cried, "Tell me the place where I can get good food."

Clever Tom told the way to his parents house. The wolf reached the place in the night. While Tom's parents were asleep, the wolf went to the kitchen and ate up all the food beyond his capacity. Now he was unable to move. He laid down on the floor. At this moment, Tom started crying from the belly. The wolf tried to stop Tom, "Please keep silence! Otherwise people would wake up." But Tom continued to cry and said to the wolf, "You have eaten to your fill and now you are enjoying. Let me also enjoy a little." So Tom raised his voice a bit louder and as a result, his parents woke up. Seeing

the wolf, they picked up weapons to kill him. Tom's father picked an axe and the mother took a sickle. The father spoke to Tom's mother, "First, I will hit with the axe and then you strike with your sickle."

Hearing him made Tom cry, "Father, I am in the belly of the wolf. Hence, take care and hit the wolf on his head."

Tom's parents did as they had been told. They killed the wolf. Thereafter, they cut open the belly of the wolf. Tom jumped out of the wolf's belly. His father picked him up and asked him how he had reached inside the wolf. Tom narrated the incidents from the time he had been sold to the strangers. Out of joy, his parents kissed him many times. They thanked God on their son's return and lived happily thereafter.

THE DRESS OF THE EMPEROR

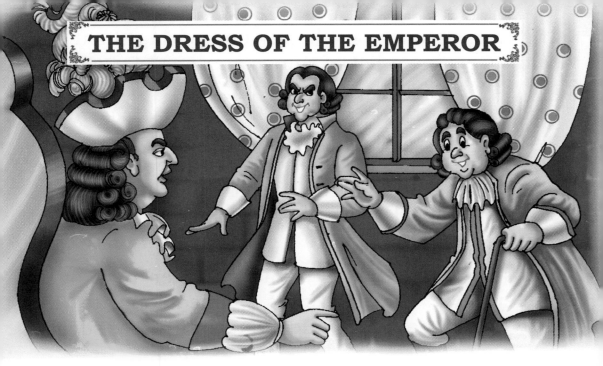

Long ago, there was a king. His palace was splendid and marvellous. The king was very fond of new dresses. Most of the times, he remained busy in selecting clothes for himself. He also invested enough money on dress materials. He was least interested in the welfare of his people. He used to go out only to show his new dresses.

One day, two swindlers came to the city. They heard about the craze of the king for new dresses and wanted to take the advantage of his obsession. Therefore, they went to the palace and saluted the king. They said, "We have come from a very far place. We are expert in weaving and would like to stitch new clothes for you. The dresses would be extraordinary and very attractive which you would not have worn before. Give us a chance to serve you and show our skills. We will prepare very special dresses for you."

The king became very happy on hearing them and said, "Give me a list of things you need for making the dresses?" The thugs said, "Silk and golden threads only." They further said, "First of all we will prepare a very special and unique dress for you. That dress can be seen only by those people who are intelligent. Hearing it, the king thought, 'It is good. I can then easily know whether a person is intelligent or a fool.'

The king ordered his prime minister to provide money and the materials immediately to the weavers, so that they could make the dresses soon.

After taking the money and other materials, both the thugs went away. They took a room on rent in the city. They also purchased a loom only to show that they were busy in preparing a dress. Whenever a visitor came to see the progress of the work, they used to pretend as if they were making clothes. However, they had not been weaving any clothes.

One day, a member of the royal family came to see

the dress, but could not see any dress. Out of fear of being called a fool, she did not disclose the reality that she actually didn't see any clothes, instead praised the weavers, "Oh! what a beautiful dress the weavers are preparing for the king!" Her words of praise for the weavers' work, prompted the prime minister to see the dress. When he reached there, the thugs said to him, "Welcome sir, see what a beautiful dress is being made for the king!" But the prime minister could not see any clothes. Then he recollected the words of the thugs that only those who were intelligent and suitable for their post could see the magical dress. Hence, he accepted the words of the thugs and nodded his head in confirmation. But the prime minister also advised the king to go to see the dress himself. He praised the thugs and said that he had never seen such a nice dress in his life before.

The king's family and courtiers also visited the weavers, but none of them wanted to be called fools. Hence, they praised the

weavers. The king was very happy with the weavers and paid even more money to them.

Now the king could not control himself. He decided to see his dress himself. One day, he reached the weavers' workshop. The thugs showed him an empty frame of the loom and said, "See your dress yourself. What a beautiful dress is this!" Hearing it, the king saw towards the empty frame but could not see any dress there. He immediately recalled the words of the weavers. Hence, he thought twice before giving his reaction. He thought, 'Why did my family and the court officials say such nice things to me. It means they all are intelligent and I am a fool." But the king did not want to disclose that he was unable to see the dress. Therefore, the king praised the dress being prepared by the weavers. He even paid them extra money to complete his dress.

At last, one day both the thugs went to the king and said, " O king! your magical dress is ready to be worn. We would bring the dress to you on any day

you wish."

The king was very eager to see his magical dress hence he asked them to bring the dress immediately. The swindlers soon brought the frames and took the king in his private room. Then, they acted as if they were  helping the king to wear the dress and said, "Oh, what a beautiful dress this is! You are looking so handsome in this dress and your real personality is now displayed. As there was no dress on the body of the king he said," It appears that I am not wearing any dress material." Both the thugs smiled and said, "We have already told you that you would not have worn such a dress before." Then they whispered to each other, 'the king seems to be a fool himself.' The king was right in his doubt that he was not wearing anything; he was totally naked. But what made the king and other people pose as if they had seen the unique dress, was the fear of being called fools.

The king stood in front of the mirror to see his personality in that dress. He was shocked to see

himself without any dress. This made him conclude that he was really a fool and not worthy of kingship. But how could he disclose this fact to others? The king was forced to praise the dress. He called all his family members, courtiers and ministers to see his dress. They were surprised to see the king naked, but all concealed this fact for the fear of being recognised as a fool and praised the dress.

The king said, "Now I want to show my dress to all the people. I will wear it again tomorrow on my birthday and take a round of the city."

Next day, the king sat in his chariot and took a round of the city. People were surprised to see the king naked. Even they thought themselves to be a fool. But in order to hide their foolishness, all praised the dress.

The king was very happy in his new dress and was sitting in his chariot with great dignity and grace. On

the way, he strutted like a child.

But there was a child among the onlookers of the king. He did not know about any magical dress. Seeing the king naked, he cried, "Oh see! the king is naked!" Hearing it all the people laughed and said, "The king is not wearing any clothes. He is naked. The sound echoed all around. The king realised that he had been cheated. He ran back out of shame. But the thugs had already escaped from the city.

A GREEDY KING

Once upon a time there was a king named Chitrasen. The people in his state were prosperous and happy. But he was very greedy and was not satisfied with the wealth he had.

One day, a youth came to his kingdom and said, "I have a proposal for you."

The very name of a proposal excited the king. He asked the youth, "Tell me about the proposal immediately." The youth replied, "I know three cities which are very prosperous. I can help you in conquering these cities."

The joy of the king knew no bounds. He asked the youth about the right time for attacking the cities. The youth replied that there should be no delay.

He further said, "O king! prepare for the attack within two days and we will proceed on the third day. When your army is ready, inform me and I will come." After this the youth left.

Thereafter, the king called his commander-in-chief and ordered him to get the army ready for a big fight. The chief of the army asked the king, "Is there a possibility of an attack?"

The king replied, "No, but we are going to attack on three rich cities. I want you to make all the preparations within two days. On the third day, we shall proceed."

The chief said, "Ok! the army would be ready on the third day."

Now the king started day-dreaming. He thought, 'My kingdom will become bigger than ever before. I will be called a prosperous king . All other kings will have no significance.'

He was very happy. He lost all his patience and was not even able to wait for two days. His commander made all the preparations for the war and informed the king. The king called a messenger and said, " Go and inform that youth immediately about our preparations. Tell him to come here and lead us to the prosperous cities."

The messenger asked, "Who is the youth? Where does he live? Please tell me his address." The king thought for a while and realised his mistake. Out of over excitement, he had forgot to ask the name and address of the youth. Irritated, he said, "Go and search for him throughout the kingdom. I cannot wait for long."

The soldiers made a thorough search for the youth but all their search went in vain. The king was very much upset to know that his men were not able to find the youth. He cursed himself for having lost the opportunity to conquer the three rich cities. He thought that due to overexcitement, he had forgot to ask the name of the cities, otherwise he could have attacked and won the cities himself. He repented for his foolishness.

He became eccentric and fell ill out of disappointment. His condition became worse day by day. Many physicians and doctors tried their best to treat the king but could not cure him. They were not even able to diagnose the disease.

The king was bed-ridden.

One day, an unknown person came to the kingdom. He met the prime minister and expressed his desire to treat the king. The prime minister said, "A number of physicians have already tried their best but failed. You may also try." So he took the stranger to the king's chamber. The stranger said to the king, "It is strange to see that you are sleeping on only one bed. Being a king, you are supposed to sleep on at least four beds" Hearing it, the king said, " What rubbish you are speaking! How can a person sleep on four beds at a time?"

The stranger argued, "Yes, you are right. But you are trying to do the same yourself. You already have a big kingdom, why were you then eager to conquer other three cities. This is nothing but greed which has destroyed your mental peace and you have become bed-ridden." The king realised his mistake and thought, 'I was a big fool as I lost mental peace due to my greed for a larger kingdom. But now I have learnt a lesson for the whole life.'

A JOURNEY OF SALEH TO SIRAJ

Once there was a trader in Baghdad named Saleh. He had inherited some money from his father who was a dealer in cereals. Saleh wanted to become rich. Therefore, he consulted one of his friends and sought his advice on his intended journey to Siraj. His friend said, "It is good that you want to undertake a journey to Siraj for expanding your business. I advise you to start dealing in sandalwood instead of cereals. You will get good returns from this business."

Saleh liked the idea. He sold all the cereal and purchased sandalwood instead. He rented 30 camels and loaded them with the sandalwood.

He started his journey to Siraj. On his way, he daydreamed of being rich. After a long journey, he reached the border of Siraj with a hope that a good fortune was waiting ahead. He met a shepherdess at the border who asked Saleh, "Who are you and from where have you come from? What has brought you here?" Saleh told the shepherdess that he had come to sell sandalwood from Baghdad. She said, "It is good, but beware of the swindlers. There are large number of swindlers in Siraj. Since you are new to this city, you need to be extra cautious. It was my duty, so I warned you."

Saleh did not take the warning seriously. However, he thanked the shepherdess and proceeded ahead. He was confident that nobody would be able to swindle him.

Saleh took shelter in an inn. Next day, he went to the market. He met a person in the market who said to him, "Hello friend, welcome to Siraj. I guessed from your dress that you were new to this city. You look like a trader. What is your business?"

Saleh said, "I have come from Baghdad to sell sandalwood. I heard that it was in great demand here. I hope that I will get a good price for my product."

The man who actually was a swindler said, "Who told you that sandalwood would get you good money here? Listen, sandalwood is very cheap here. It is considered to be an ordinary wood meant for fuel only. You won't make a good business with this. You will have to sell the wood at an ordinary price."

Saleh was disappointed to hear the words. All his hope to make a fortune had shattered.

Seeing him upset, the swindler now tried to take the advantage of the situation. He said, " My friend, do not lose heart. If you agree, I am ready to purchase all your sandalwood for one gold coin. This is the best price for your sandal. It is a good bargain. So do not think. Sell the sandalwood immediately."

Saleh said, "No! the price is too low, and it is worth a lot of money. I have invested all my assets on the sandalwood."

The swindler said angrily, "Don't be silly, I am paying the correct price. Others would not even take it free. Do you understand me?"

He continued to say, "I am your friend and I want to help you. I have many friends here. They will

arrange some work for you and you can earn here during your stay. Do not worry and take it easy."

Saleh failed to understand anything. However, he accepted the offer of the swindler.

The swindler was very happy as he was successful in his plan. He purchased all the sandalwood for one gold coin and resold it for a big profit.

On the other hand, Saleh was sitting on the roadside and was very sad. He was thinking how he had been swindled. He decided to be more cautious.

Next day, when he was going to the market, he recollected the warning of the shepherdess. He was more cautious now. As he was passing by a shop, someone caught his arm from behind . He looked behind and saw a beggar who was blind. The beggar cried, "I have caught the thief who blinded me and robbed me of my money!"

Saleh was surprised and said, "What are you saying? I have never seen you before. I came here yesterday from Baghdad." But nobody was ready to hear Saleh as it was a custom to swindle the strangers. Soon, a big crowd gathered there. Saleh became nervous.

At this moment, a man came forward from the crowd and said to the begger, "Please keep silence. Let me solve the problem. I know your blame is true and this man will have to pay your money back." Helpless, Saleh could not prove his innocence and was compelled to give the money to the beggar.

Saleh went back to the inn. On his way, he went to a cobbler to get his shoe repaired. To his surprise, the cobbler wanted an amount equal to the price of a new shoe. Already in low sprit, he did not argue and paid the demanded amount for the repair.

On his way to the inn, he saw the shepherdess sitting on a stone. He went there and narrated all that had happened to him. The shepherdess said, "I had already warned you, but you did not take me seriously. Anyway, go to the businessman outside the city. He is the leader of the swindlers. Try to find out their next step. May

God help you to get your money back!"

Saleh thanked the shepherdess and proceeded towards the place that she had mentioned. There he saw the leader sitting on a mat in front of a rock. He hid himself behind the rock. He saw that all the Swindlers along with those who had swindled him—the one who had purchased his sandalwood, the beggar and his helper, the cobbler and the owner of the inn, etc, were gathered there.

The leader said to his men, "Tell me how much you have earned today."

One swindler said, "I swindled a businessman of Baghdad. I purchased his sandalwood at a nominal price by convincing him that it is very cheap here. Thereafter, I sold it at a high price and earned huge profits. You'll be happy to know that my achievements are worth praising."

The leader said, "Well done my friend! Keep it up."

Then he asked the others to give the detail of their achievements.

Now the beggar said, "I met a stranger on the road. His dress told that he was a rich man. So I caught his hand and blamed him for making me blind and stealing my money. I cried and was able to collect the crowd. He had to pay under pressure. Tell me, is it not a good achievement?"

The leader said, "Your work is also worth praising. You have done well. I wish you good luck."

Then the cobbler said, "I also cheated a stranger who had come to me for the repairing his shoes. He seemed to be very rich, and that is why I charged thrice of my labour. Would you not praise me?" The leader said, "Though you could not earn much, like your friends but still you did well. You are new in this line. Slowly, you will also come to their level." The next swindler was the owner of the inn. He disclosed

that he charged a stranger a lot of money. Hearing the conversation, Saleh concluded that all the people of the city were swindlers. They tried their best to cheat the strangers. 'I must leave this city immediately," thought Saleh.

As Saleh was thinking of his next move, he heard the leader telling the owner of the inn "Go to our secret cave on the hill and verify if all the wealth is safe. In case the strangers came to know about our hidden wealth, they would take away all our possessions."

The owner of the inn said, "I will go immediately to check."

Later the leader said to the cobbler, business man and the beggar to go for their respective works. All of them left.

Saleh decided to follow the owner of the inn who was going to check the secret treasure. He thought, 'Now I hope my luck will change. I will steal their wealth

and take the revenge.' So he followed him. On reaching the hill, the innkeeper moved a stone aside and entered a cave through a narrow passage. Saleh thought, 'It must be the cave that has swindled wealth. I must wait for the innkeeper's departure. Thereafter, I will enter the cave and find out what is there inside the cave.' After some time, the innkeeper left to meet his leader. Saleh took the advantage of the situation and entered the cave. He was surprised to see the boxes full of silver and gold coins. After seeing the huge wealth, he decided to come again with his camels.

He quickly came out and rushed to the inn. He prepared himself for the return journey. Next day, he reached the cave early in the morning with his camels. He loaded them with all the wealth of the cave and proceeded to Baghdad.

He met the shepherdess on his way home. The shepherdess asked, "Are you going back to Baghdad?

Would you not stay for some more time in our city?" Saleh said to the shepherdess, "I am thankful to you for your advice. I got the treasure with your help."

The shepherdess asked, "Have you got your sandalwood back?" Saleh smiled and said, "I have got more money than the value of the sandalwood." Thereafter, Saleh told everything to the shepherdess. Knowing everything, the shepherdess said, "Well done! You have given a good lesson to the swindlers. A theft in the house of a thief is not unethical."

Thereafter, Saleh offered a bag of gold coins to the shepherdess for her help. The shepherdess accepted it and thanked him, "Do not think that all the people of Siraj are bad. There are nice and good people as well. So tell the people of Baghdad that they should also visit Siraj at their convenience." Saleh smiled and nodded his head. And he returned to Baghdad with his camels loaded with the wealth.

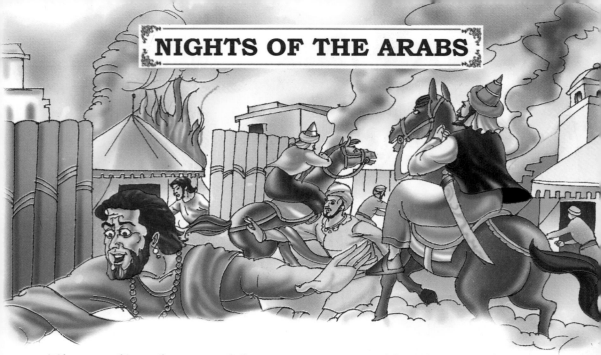

There lived a noble man named Abu Sabir in a village of Arabia. He was very intelligent, brave and kind. He had deep faith in God and believed that God is always kind to everyone and never made anyone suffer.

One day, some robbers killed an official of the Sultan near the village of Abu Sabir. When the Sultan came to know about the murder of his officer, he got furious and ordered his commander-in-chief to set the whole village on fire.

On the order of the Sultan, the commander-in-chief reached the village and ordered his soldiers, "Set all the houses on fire. Before doing it, you can even rob the villagers of their valuables."

The soldiers destroyed all the houses one by one. The house of Abu Sabir was also among them. He was helplessly seeing his house being destroyed and burnt. His wife said, "All our savings have turned to

ashes and we have become beggars. What should we do now?" She further said, "You should go to the Sultan and tell him how long we have been serving him and despite all that his soldiers have destroyed our house. It is unfair." "Really this act of the Sultan is totally barbarous. It is not just. The almighty God is observing everything. He will punish the Sultan for his misdeeds," added Abu.

Unfortunately a spy heard their conversation and told the Sultan everything they spoke of him.

Hearing the spy, the Sultan got furious. He shouted, " How Abu dared to speak against me! I myself will go there and punish Abu."

The Sultan went to the village of Abu and ordered the soldiers, "Throw all the family members of Abu out of the house and destroy the house completely."

The soldiers destroyed the house. Abu's wife began to cry bitterly. But Abu consoled her saying, " Have faith in God and keep patience. God will set everything right." Thereafter, Abu left that village along with his two sons and wife.

On their way, a gang of robbers stopped them. When they found nothing in Abu's possession, they abducted both his sons.

Abu's wife was greatly shocked after the abduction of her sons. Abu consoled her and said to God looking above, "Oh God! it is too much. Be kind to us and get us out of this trouble."

They continued to proceed further. It was almost evening when they reached a village. Abu said to his wife, " Stay here. I am going to find out a suitable where we can spend the night." Abu went to the village leaving his wife alone at the roadside.

As soon as Abu left his wife alone, a horseman happened to pass by that route. Seeing a beautiful woman alone, he kidnapped her. She disclosed her marital status and pleaded the horseman . to leave her. But the horseman ignored her appeal and took her away forcibly.

She wrote 'kidnapped' on the sand. When Abu returned, he read the word. He became unconscious and when he regained consciousness, he spoke out in disgust, "Oh God! Why are you putting me to a test again and again?"

Now Abu was all alone and sad. He moved aimlessly on the road. After some time, he reached a city where a big building was being constructed for the Sultan of that territory. Abu got a job there as a labourer.

One day, a labourer fell from the top of the building and got injured. Abu rushed to the labourer and comforted him, "Do not worry. Everything would set right soon. Believe in God."

The injured labourer was totally disappointed and said, "I am already in trouble. How can I have patience and wait for the justice of God."

Abu continued, "Nothing would move without the consent of god. If He desires, a man may fall in a ditch or could achieve a throne." Unfortunately, the

Sultan who was present there heard Abu. He got angry and said, "I will throw you into the ditch and see how you would be able to get the throne." He ordered his soldiers to put Abu into the death cell. As per his order, the soldiers pushed Abu into the death cell and said, "Go and live with the exiled brother of the Sultan in the cell."

The life in the underground cell was miserable. Sultan used to keep his enemies in the cell. Very little food was served there. Abu was fed up with the life there and prayed, "Oh God, be kind and take me out of this cell."

On the other side, the atrocities of the Sultan were increasing. The people who disliked him earlier now began to hate him.

One day, an angry opponent murdered the Sultan. The people in opposition said, "The tyrant is finished. Let us take the brother of the Sultan out of the death cell and crown him as the new Sultan." Actually they did not know that the brother of the Sultan was dead.

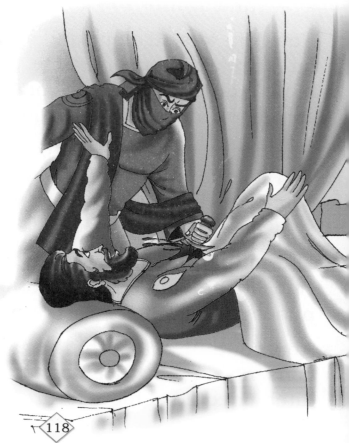

They released Abu Sabir as the brother of the Sultan and crowned him the new Sultan of the kingdom.

While sitting on the throne, Abu thanked God and said, "Oh God! You are great. Really you can make anybody a king. Even a person from a ditch can be the king."

Abu, at first, searched for the robbers in the kingdom and hanged them all and got his sons back. He exclaimed with joy, "My sons, I hope I will certainly get back your mother as well, who had been kidnapped earlier."

One day, when the Sultan Abu was passing through a village, he saw a rich person who was beating a woman. The rich man wanted to sell that woman as a slave. When he reached there, he recognised the woman as his lost wife. He immediately got the man arrested and brought his wife to his palace. He thanked the Almighty who reunited him with his

sons and wife. Later on, he also ordered to hang the guilty man who was trying to sell his wife as a slave. Then Abu proceeded to attack the tyrant Sultan who has destroyed his house. He defeated him and then killed him.

One day, while Abu was sitting in his court, he announced before all the courtiers, " Some of you might be suspecting that I may prove to be a tyrant like the dead Sultan. But you will be surprised to know that I am not the brother of the dead Sultan."

Then Abu narrated the whole story. He further said that he always waited for the right time and opportunity to do justice. The robbers were given the death penalty because they deserved it.

All the courtiers welcomed Abu and praised his ability and brave actions. They unanimously declared Abu as their new Sultan.

THE WICKED CAMEL

During the ancient times, the Arabs mainly used camels as a means of transport because they could walk very fast in the desert sand and could tolerate intense heat and survive without food and water for many days.

Once an Arab desired to go to another city for his business. He got his camel ready for the journey and loaded all the luggage onto the camel. He also loaded a tent on the back of the camel, so that he could spend the cold night in the desert comfortably.

In the evening, the businessman pitched the tent in the desert and tied his camel outside. The nights of the desert are very cold. The Arab went inside the tent to sleep leaving the camel outside. The camel shivered with cold and did not like the way his master behaved. He said to his master, "Let me put my head inside the tent as there is too much cold outside. I will not trouble you."

The Arab was kind-hearted. He allowed the camel to keep his head inside the tent and then slept.

After some time, the camel again said, "Master, my neck is about to freeze due to cold. Please allow me to keep the neck inside."

The Arab kindly said, "Okay," and went off to sleep. After some time camel again said, "My legs are chilled with cold. I have to walk tomorrow. Let me keep the legs inside."

Arab thought, 'The camel is right' He folded his legs and asked the camel to keep his legs inside the tent.

This way the cunning camel had taken the possession of more than half of the tent. He now thought, 'My master is a big fool. He is too kind and I must take advantage of his kindness.'

He said to his master, "O kind master, my hump is iced with cold. I am shivering with cold and I request you to adjust my hump inside the tent. Please shift a bit and adjust me."

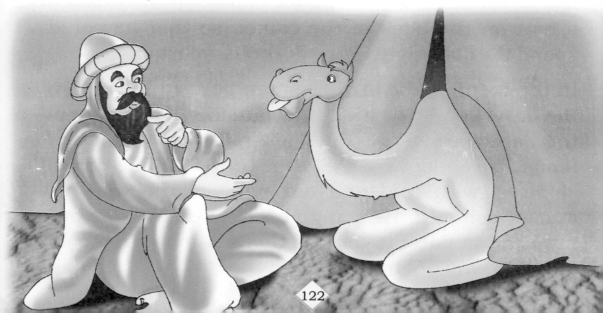

The kind-hearted Arab thought that the camel should be allowed to enter the tent. He shifted a little more to adjust the camel in the tent. Now only the back legs of the camel were outside the tent.

The camel was very warm inside the tent. Now the camel thought to bring the hind legs also into the tent because the camel was feeling cold only on his hind legs. So he decided to push his master outside the tent and waited for such an opportunity. Soon his master slept and the camel pushed him gently outside the tent.

The camel slept comfortably inside the tent, while the poor Arab stayed outside the tent and shivered for the rest of the night. The days passed smoothly for the kind-hearted man. But the reward for his kindness was that he had to spend the whole night in the cold of the desert.

Once a beggar was roaming in the streets of Baghdad. While roaming, he stood in front of a large and beautiful house and thought, 'The owner of this house must be a rich person. I expect good food from here.' Thus, he went straight to the gatekeeper and asked his permission to go in for food." He allowed the beggar to go inside and also told that he would get anything he wished. So the beggar was pleased and asked, "Who is your master?"

The gatekeeper said, "My master is a very rich and powerful person. He belongs to a very influential family of Bermisai."

The beggar went inside. He reached a big hall past a beautiful garden. He was charmed to see the beautiful paintings and other decorative pieces on the wall. There were colourful curtains on the windows and doors. Across the hall there was a beautiful throne and an old man was sitting on it.

His beard was long and black.

Seeing the beggar, the old man said, "Yes, my friend! What do you want?" The beggar said, "I am very hungry. I have not eaten for the last two days. Will you please give me some food?"

The old man said, "Of course! You will certainly get food. It is a matter of shame for me if anyone is hungry in the city. Today, you will have meal with me."

The old man then asked one of his servants, "Bring water in a pot for my friend to wash his hands." But when the beggar got up to wash his hands he saw no pot of water. But the old man was acting as if he was pouring water from a jug. The beggar understood that he was being befooled but acted as if he was washing his hands. Then the old man asked the servant to serve the food. All the servants began acting as if they were putting dishes on the table. But no food was visible. The old man acted as though he was eating and even asked the beggar to start eating. Seeing all this drama, the beggar was

very disappointed. But even then, he acted as if he was having a delicious meal.

The beggar guessed that this man must have befooled many other people in the same way. He concluded that he was fond of doing this with all strangers.

Then he told the old man, "I have never eaten such a tasty food in my life!" The old man asked the servants to bring some sweets for the guest. The servants acted as if they were serving sweets to the beggar. The beggar also acted as if he was eating them. Thereafter, he said to the old man that he had eaten enough and did not want more. But the old man said, "You have to take a glass of wine with me," and asked his servant to serve the wine to the guest. The servants again acted as if wine was being served. The old man acted as if he was offering a glass of it to the guest. So the beggar also acted accordingly and showed that he was drinking the wine. He even acted

as if he had drunk a lot because he wanted to teach a lesson to the old man. As if acting like a drunkard, the beggar gave a hard blow with his fist to his host and repeated it thrice. The old man cried with pain, "Oh you rascal! Why are you beating me?" The beggar said, "You welcomed me and served me delicious food. That was good. But after drinking wine, I have lost control of my senses. But you are so great and kind. I am sure you would pardon me."

To this, the old man laughed and said, "I have been fooling people for a long time, but no one dared to behave like this. However, I am happy with you and want to make you my friend. We will really take food now." Then he asked his servants to serve food. The beggar enjoyed the food and accepted the friendship of the old man. Since then, they remained friends throughout their lives.

THE OLD WOMAN AND DOCTOR

Once, there lived an old woman in a city. Her husband had died and she had no child either. She lived all alone in her house. She always kept herself busy in decorating the house. She had hung beautiful paintings on the walls. She was in the habit of purchasing ornamental items. She was very happy to see the beauty of her house.

One day, all of a sudden, she felt some serious problem in her eyes and she was unable to see things clearly. After some time her vision got impaired a little. She went to a doctor and said, "Doctor, I am not able to see clearly. It appears that I will become blind soon if not cured. Can you treat my eyes so that I see clearly like before?" The Doctor

replied, "Why not, but it will take some time to cure your eyes completely."

The old woman said, " I will pay a good fee to you if you cure my eyes perfectly."

The doctor started treating the old lady. When he saw the expensive paintings and other decorative items in her house, he decided to steal them. He kept the old lady's eyes bandaged during the treatment. Whenever he visited the lady, he would put some medicine in her eyes, covered them back and before leaving, he would take away some of the paintings or decorative items.

Now the time came when the doctor unfolded the lady's eyes. Her eyes were cured and she could see clearly. But she was shocked to see her walls empty. All the precious paintings and other adorned items were missing. She understood everything and said to the doctor, "You say that my eyes are fine, but I can't see my paintings. It means my eyes are still not cured. So I am not going to pay you any fee."

The doctor filed a suit in the court of law against the old woman. In the court, the doctor claimed for the fee for the treatment of her eyes and asked for justice. The old lady was summoned and asked to put her argument before the judge in the court for not making the payment to the doctor.

The old lady said, "Honourable sir, it is true that I had promised to pay a good amount to the doctor for the treatment of my eyes." "Then why didn't you make the payment?" inquired the judge. The lady clarified, "Sir before the treatment started, there were many paintings and other precious items in my house. After the treatment, none can be seen. Hence, I concluded that my eyes are not yet cured. Therefore, the doctor has no right to ask me for the fee." The judge was surprised to hear the argument of the old lady. He understood what actually had happened and dismissed the claim of the doctor.

FISHERMAN AND HIS FLUTE

Once there was a fisherman who lived with his wife. He was also a good flute player. The melodious music of his flute, made children gather and dance around him. Whosoever heard his flute could not help praising the fisherman.

One day, he thought, 'I am an expert flute player. I will sit near the river and play the flute for the fishes. This way, a lot of fishes would be caught without using the net.' The next day, he went to the river and played the flute. But no fish came out. He again tried but failed to attract any fish. He thought, 'It seems that the fishes have gone deep in the water that is why they can not hear the flute. This time, I will play the flute more loudly to attract them'. With this thought he played his flute loudly again and again. But all in vain. Even the best tune on the flute brought no result to him.

He continued to play the flute many times more louder than before. But it all proved to be a wastage of time and energy. He got disappointed. He decided to return empty-handed. But before that he thought of trying once again. But still he got nothing. He concluded that the fishes had gone for a deep sleep and hence, they could not hear the flute. At last, he picked his empty basket and came back to his house.

Seeing the basket empty, his wife said, "You have come without any fish. Now what will we eat today? Go and try again." The fisherman narrated all that had happened. Angered, his wife said, "Take the net instead of the flute."

The fisherman took the net and went again to the river and threw the net into the river to catch fish. Luckily, many fish were entrapped in the net. He put them into the basket and threw the net again. This

time also he caught a large number of fish. He collected them also. The fish were twisting and tossing in the basket due to the lack of water. At this, the fisherman said, "You big fools! Why did you not dance to my flute's music?"

He picked up the basket and came back home. His wife was waiting for him. She was happy to see so many fish and said, " Well done! You have brought a lot of fish today. It must be the result of your hard labour." She further said, "You were trying to catch fish through the flute's music, but you forgot that nothing is gained without efforts. And beating around the bush gives no result. It is true that you are a very good flute player, but that is not useful for catching fish." The fisherman agreed and said, "You are right. Nothing is gained without hard labour. It is a great lesson one must learn."

Bisher was a kind and generous person. He was a moneylender and banker. He was very honest in his dealings. He used to help others in their distress and was respected in the society. People used to visit him frequently. Even the caliph (king) respected him. He was doing good business. He always believed in the almighty God and was grateful to Him.

Everything was going well, but all of a sudden bad luck knocked at his door. People stopped paying the loan back. His financial condition became grim because he had never kept the record of the debtors. So he could not lay claim for his money in the court of the Governor. He was disappointed and could not decide what to do; how to deal with this trouble.

As Bisher's bad days were on, rumours spread in the society. People talked different things about Bisher. Some said he was insolvent, while others said he had become very poor. It is no use to go to an impoverished man. It is better to keep away from such a person. Poor Bisher was depressed to think

of his dark future.

One day while he was feeling sad and lonely, his wife came and said, "It is no use sitting idle. Have courage and do something else."

Bisher got some relief and thought deeply about it. Then he slept. While he was sleeping someone knocked at the door. At first, he did not pay attention, but knocking continued until he opened the door. He was surprised to see a man who had his face covered.

Bisher asked the stranger, "Who are you? What are you doing here? Do you need any help?"

The stranger replied, "My name is not important. Just consider me as your friend. I know you are in trouble and I have come here to help you." The stranger then gave a bag to Bisher and said, "Take this bag. This will help you get out of the trouble and your bad days would be over soon."

Bisher was hesitating to take the bag from a stranger and was staring at him.

The stranger felt

his hesitation and clarified, "Don't hesitate to accept this bag. I help those who help others. It is my duty to help my friends when they are in distress."

The stranger left after handing the bag to Bisher. Thereafter, Bisher went to his room with the bag. He asked his wife to light the lamp to see what was there in the bag but there was no oil at home. They decided to check the bag in the morning and slept.

Next morning, the first thing that Bisher did was to open the bag. His wife was also standing near him and was eager to know what was there in the bag.

As soon as they opened the bag, their eyes widened to see gold dinars in it. His wife said, "Oh! these are dinars."

Bisher and his wife were thrilled and said that this much money would revive their status again. Bisher said to his wife, "I will repay the loan borrowed from other moneylenders and would be able to restart the

business."

With the timely help from the stranger, Bisher settled in the business again. He became rich. People also returned their dues to Bisher. Now he was doing good in his business.

One day, he was called by the caliph. When he reached the palace, the caliph said, "What is the matter? Where had you been for so long?"

Bisher replied, "I was in trouble so I could not come to pay visit to you."

Then he narrated the whole incident to the caliph and disclosed how a stranger had helped him and since then he is progressing well.

The caliph asked out of eagerness, "Who was that stranger? If you happen to meet him again, bring him to me."

Bisher said, "I do not know him. He only told me that he help those who help others."

The caliph was very much impressed by Bisher. He

said to Bisher, "The governor of Mesopotamia had not deposited the revenue and hence, I eliminated him. Now I wish to send you there as the new governor. Go there and take the charge."

Bisher thanked the caliph and said, "You have given me a chance to serve you."

Bisher went to Mesopotamia. The governor of Mesopotamia Faiyyaz, was a friend of Bisher. Bisher delivered the message of the caliph to him. Faiyyaz welcomed him and resigned from the post. Bisher found that Faiyyaz had misused the fund. No matter that he was his friend, but friendship was not above the law. So he asked Faiyyaz to return the money which he had earned by treachery.

But Faiyyaz said that he had no money to return. So Bisher said, "I am helpless. You will have to go to prison till the money is recovered." Faiyyaz was sent to prison.

One day, Bisher received a letter by an unknown person. He was very upset to

read the content. The letter said, "Bisher, won't you like to be a messiah and help the messiah who help others in their distress?"

After reading the letter, Bisher understood everything. The letter was written by the wife of the deposed governor Faiyyaz. He immediately sent for Faiyyaz.

As soon as Faiyyaz came, Bisher hugged him warmly and said, "Dear friend, I should be in prison, not you. You are a messiah. Why didn't you tell this fact earlier."

Faiyyaz said that he was not interested in disclosing the fact. But his wife insisted on writing and telling everything to Bisher.

Now Bisher recollected his promise made to the caliph. He had promised the caliph to bring the messiah before him who had helped him in his bad days.

Bisher went to meet caliph with Faiyyaz. He presented his friend before the caliph and said, "I have found the messiah who had helped me in my bad days. Since you had

wished to meet the messiah, I have brought him here. He is none other than your deposed governor and my friend Faiyyaz."

The caliph was very impressed and pleased with Faiyyaz. He praised Faiyyaz and reappointed him as the governor of Mesopotamia. Faiyyaz thanked the caliph and bowed to him.

Then the caliph asked Bisher to go to Arminia as a governor and take the charge immediately. Bisher thanked the caliph.

Seeing the generosity of the caliph, Faiyyaz thought, 'It is heavenly to help those who help others'. Now both Bisher and Faiyyaz left to take charge of their respective posts happily.

A WISE JACKAL

Long ago, there was a forest called Kanha in which a variety of wild animals lived together. The king of the forest was a lion.

Once a jackal, a wolf and the lion joined their hands and became friends. Since then, they lived together and shared everything. One day when they were busy gossiping, the jackal said, "Friends, if we all hunt together, we can enjoy a good feast everyday."

Both the lion and the wolf agreed to the proposal of the jackal. The lion said, "Since you have got me as your friend, see how I will give you a feast of fresh meat every day." The lion roared at the top of his voice. Hearing the loud roar, both the wolf and the jackal got frightened. Though they were happy to have the company of lion, yet they were afraid of his anger. From that day, they continued to hunt together and share the fresh meat. The regularity of

eating fresh meat made them stout and healthy.

One day, after hunting, while all the friends were sitting together, the lion said to the wolf, "Today, you divide the prey." The wolf felt proud. He divided the meat equally among all. Seeing an equal share for each, the lion got angry and said to the wolf, "How dare you take an equal share? You have forgotten your status. There is no comparison between you and me." So the lion killed the wolf. Then the lion said to the jackal, "Now, it is your turn to divide the prey."

The jackal was trembling with fear. He could only say 'Yes.' He made two shares and gave the big one to the lion. This pleased the lion. He said, "Well done! you have not repeated the folly of the wolf." The jackal said, "O king of the forest! I had learnt the lesson." Then they both fed on their share happily.

Later the jackal decided not to go on with this friendship with the lion. He realised the fact that friendship between unequals is transitory.

PRIDE LEADS TO DESTRUCTION

Once Ram Murti was going to his village after a gap of ten years. When he was about to enter the village, a goat

with long horns came near him and bleated. Seeing the goat, Ram Murti stopped and said to himself vainly, "Oh! I am a well-known personality. Even this goat knows me well and is welcoming me."

!Hearing him, a shopkeeper of the roadside said to Ram Murti, "O brother! Run away from here. Otherwise this goat will attack and will get hurt."

But Ram Murti ignored the shopkeeper's advice and said, " What do you mean ? The goat will hurt me? She can't do it."

Ram Murti was still standing before the goat and continued, "You do not know animals have a sixth sense to recognise a worthy person, and this goat has recognised me as a great personality. See how she is still standing with her head down." Just as he finished boasting, the goat attacked and wounded

him. He fell on the ground and so did his bag. All his things lay scattered on the road. The shopkeeper rushed to help him. By then the goat had gone away. He picked the bag and helped Ram Murti to get up and asked if he was seriously injured.

Ram Murti said, "You were right. I should have followed your advice. But I was driven by pride and got hurt in return."

It is rightly said that pride is the cause of destruction.